It's My Year
Passbook

Written by Elizabeth Bennett
Illustrated and designed by Deena Fleming

an imprint of
■SCHOLASTIC
www.scholastic.com

Published by Tangerine Press, an imprint of Scholastic Inc.,
557 Broadway, New York, NY 10012

11 10 9 8 7 6 5 4 3 2

ISBN: 978-0-545-22112-2

Printed and bound in China

Scholastic Canada Ltd.
Markham, Ontario

Scholastic Australia Pty. Ltd
Gosford NSW

Scholastic New Zealand Ltd.
Greenmount, Auckland

Attention friends!

The book you are holding is very important. It's going to be filled with facts, favorites, fears, and future dreams of you and all my friends. So grab a pencil and a couple of minutes. Flip through the pages and fill in your answers. Then pass it along to another friend.

Don't hold anything back – I expect your complete honesty!

Here's how it works:

- Pick one of the colors on the next page and write your name next to it.
- Look in the back of the book for the stickers that match your color.
- Flip through this book and find the questions you want to answer.
- You don't have to write on every page – just pick your favorites!
- Put your sticker next to your answers in the circles.
- If you run out of stickers, don't worry. Use a crayon or colored pencil to leave your mark; or just write your initials.

Sign in here!

Write your name next to your color.

Lanisha

Lanisha

Don't forget you can use colored pencils, too! Make your mark.

After this book makes
its rounds, please return
to ME!

Lanisha Price after
_____
(name)
GES
_____
(school)
semtember 31st, 2010
_____
(date)

First Things First

Nickname _Brandon_

Email address _____

Phone number _____

IM _____

IM _____

Phone number _____

Email address _____

Nickname _____

Nickname _Maric (Hannah)_

Email address _____

Phone number _443-239-0641_

IM _____

IM _____

Phone number _____

Email address _____

Nickname _____

Nickname _____

Email address _____

Phone number _____

IM _____

Nickname _____
Email address _____
Phone number _____
IM _____

Nickname _____
Email address _____
Phone number _____
IM _____

IM _____
Phone number _____
Email address _____
Nickname _____

Nickname _____
Email address _____
Phone number _____
IM _____

IM _____
Phone number _____
Email address _____
Nickname _____

Nickname |

Email address

Phone number

IM

Nickname K

Email address

Phone number

IM

Nickname

Email address

Phone number

IM

Nickname

Email address

Phone number

IM

Nickname

Email address

Phone number

IM

Nickname _____

Email address _____

Phone number_____

IM _____

Nickname _____

Email address _____

Phone number_____

IM _____

Nickname _____

Email address _____

Phone number_____

IM _____

Nickname _____

Email address _____

Phone number_____

IM _____

Nickname _____

Email address _____

Phone number_____

IM _____

If you could pick your own name, What would it be?

What's your favorite expression?

OMG!

- ⊘ g+g
- ✓ LOL
- ⬤ O ma
- ✓ Idk
- ○ JTg
- ○ I de

Dig down deep!

What is your favorite thing about yourself?
_____
_____

What are you the most proud of?
_____
_____
_____
_____

What is your favorite thing about yourself?
_____
_____

What are you the most proud of?
_____
_____
_____
_____

What is your favorite thing about yourself?

_____

_____

What are you the most proud of?

_____

_____

_____

_____

What is your favorite thing about yourself?

_____

_____

What are you the most proud of?

_____

_____

_____

What is your favorite thing about yourself?

_____

_____

What are you the most proud of?

_____

_____

_____

_____

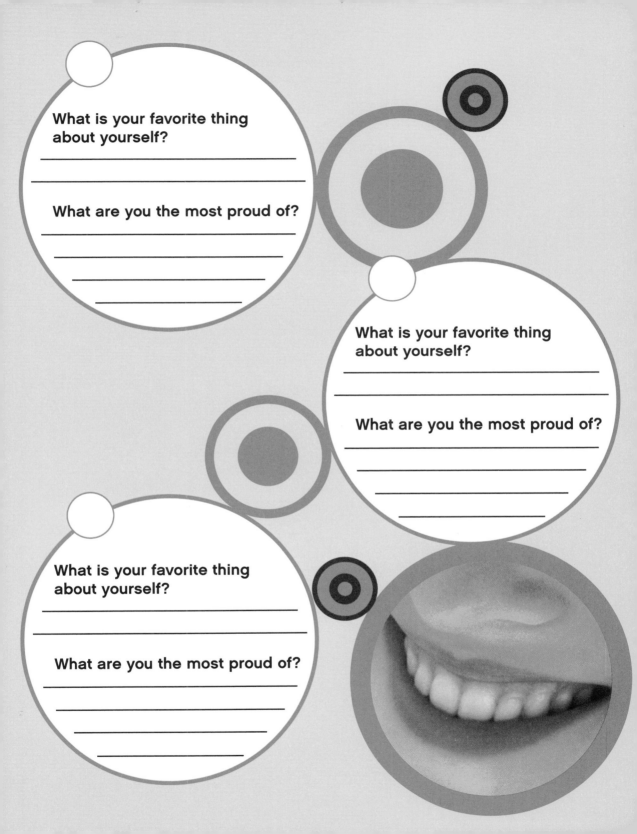

What is your favorite thing about yourself?

Score scoore

What are you the most proud of?

What is your favorite thing about yourself?

That I can cheer

What are you the most proud of?

I can cheer

What is your favorite thing about yourself?

What are you the most proud of?

What is your favorite thing about yourself?

_____

_____

What are you the most proud of?

_____

_____

_____

_____

What is your favorite thing about yourself?

_____

_____

What are you the most proud of?

_____

_____

_____

_____

What is your favorite thing about yourself?

_____

_____

What are you the most proud of?

_____

_____

_____

_____

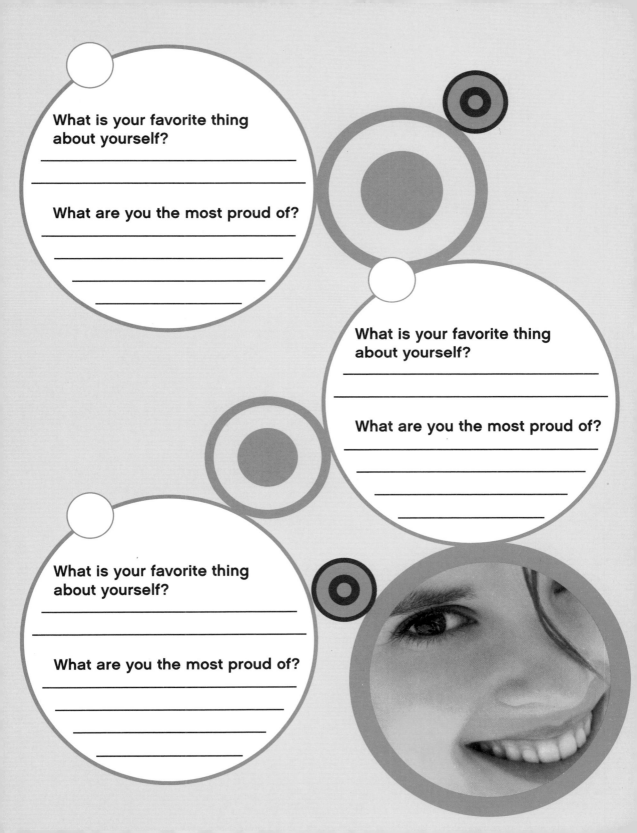

FIND YOUR INNER ARTIST —

draw a self-portrait!

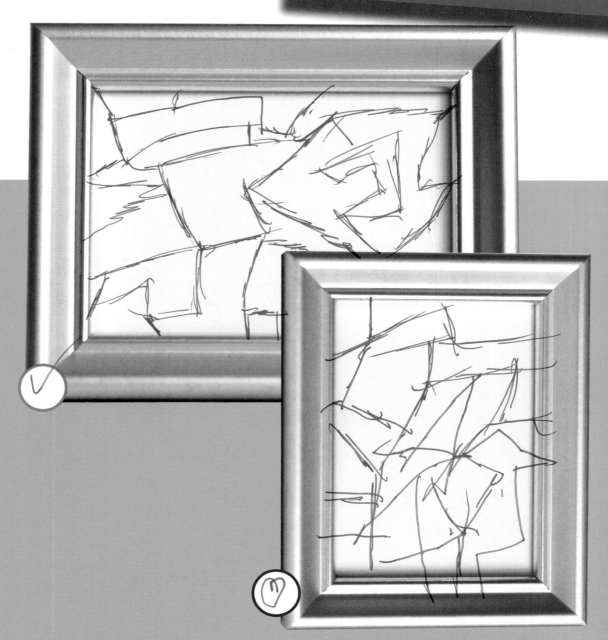

Friends Forever!

WHO IS YOUR B.F.F.?

WHO IS YOUR B.F.F.?

WHO IS YOUR B.F.F.?

WHO IS YOUR B.F.F.?

WHO IS YOUR B.F.F.?

WHO IS YOUR B.F.F.?

WHO IS YOUR B.F.F.?

What is your favorite thing to do with your friends?

☑ Go to the movies.
☑ Get something to eat.
☑ Get some exercise.
☐ Just chill.

☐ Go to the movies.
☐ Get something to eat.
☐ Get some exercise.
☐ Just chill.

☐ Go to the movies.
☐ Get something to eat.
☑ Get some exercise.
☑ Just chill.

☐ Go to the movies.
☐ Get something to eat.
☐ Get some exercise.
☐ Just chill.

246892
246891

ADMIT ONE

246891

- Go to the movies.
- Get something to eat.
- Get some exercise.
- Just chill.

- Go to the movies.
- Get something to eat.
- Get some exercise.
- Just chill.

- Go to the movies.
- Get something to eat.
- Get some exercise.
- Just chill.

- Go to the movies.
- Get something to eat.
- Get some exercise.
- Just chill.

- Go to the movies.
- Get something to eat.
- Get some exercise.
- Just chill.

- Go to the movies.
- Get something to eat.
- Get some exercise.
- Just chill.

- Go to the movies.
- Get something to eat.
- Get some exercise.
- Just chill.

- Go to the movies.
- Get something to eat.
- Get some exercise.
- Just chill.

- Go to the movies.
- Get something to eat.
- Get some exercise.
- Just chill.

- Go to the movies.
- Get something to eat.
- Get some exercise.
- Just chill.

- Go to the movies.
- Get something to eat.
- Get some exercise.
- Just chill.

- Go to the movies.
- Get something to eat.
- Get some exercise.
- Just chill.

WHO HAVE YOU BEEN FRIENDS WITH THE LONGEST?
_____
WHERE DID YOU MEET?_____
_____
_____
HOW MANY YEARS HAVE YOU BEEN FRIENDS?_____

WHO HAVE YOU BEEN FRIENDS WITH THE LONGEST?
_____
WHERE DID YOU MEET?_____
_____
HOW MANY YEARS HAVE YOU BEEN FRIENDS?_____

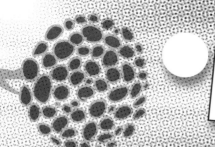

WHO HAVE YOU BEEN FRIENDS WITH THE LONGEST?
arees
WHERE DID YOU MEET? *at fisher manel*
_____
HOW MANY YEARS HAVE YOU BEEN FRIENDS? *11 years*

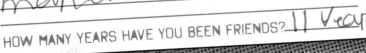

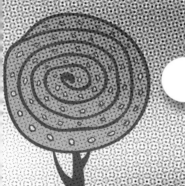

WHO HAVE YOU BEEN FRIENDS WITH THE LONGEST?
_____
WHERE DID YOU MEET?_____
_____
HOW MANY YEARS HAVE YOU BEEN FRIENDS?_____

WHO HAVE YOU BEEN FRIENDS WITH THE LONGEST? _____

WHERE DID YOU MEET? _____

_____

HOW MANY YEARS HAVE YOU BEEN FRIENDS? _____

WHO HAVE YOU BEEN FRIENDS WITH THE LONGEST? _____

WHERE DID YOU MEET? _____

_____

HOW MANY YEARS HAVE YOU BEEN FRIENDS? _____

WHO HAVE YOU BEEN FRIENDS WITH THE LONGEST? _____

WHERE DID YOU MEET? _____

_____

HOW MANY YEARS HAVE YOU BEEN FRIENDS? _____

WHO HAVE YOU BEEN FRIENDS WITH THE LONGEST? _____

WHERE DID YOU MEET? _____

_____

HOW MANY YEARS HAVE YOU BEEN FRIENDS? _____

WHO HAVE YOU BEEN FRIENDS WITH THE LONGEST?
_____

WHERE DID YOU MEET?_____
_____

HOW MANY YEARS HAVE YOU BEEN FRIENDS?_____

WHO HAVE YOU BEEN FRIENDS WITH THE LONGEST?
_____

WHERE DID YOU MEET?_____
_____

HOW MANY YEARS HAVE YOU BEEN FRIENDS?_____

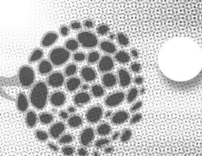

WHO HAVE YOU BEEN FRIENDS WITH THE LONGEST?
_____

WHERE DID YOU MEET?_____
_____

HOW MANY YEARS HAVE YOU BEEN FRIENDS?_____

WHO HAVE YOU BEEN FRIENDS WITH THE LONGEST?
_____

WHERE DID YOU MEET?_____
_____

HOW MANY YEARS HAVE YOU BEEN FRIENDS?_____

WHO HAVE YOU BEEN FRIENDS WITH THE LONGEST?

WHERE DID YOU MEET?

HOW MANY YEARS HAVE YOU BEEN FRIENDS?

WHO HAVE YOU BEEN FRIENDS WITH THE LONGEST?
Arlew

WHERE DID YOU MEET? Fisherman

HOW MANY YEARS HAVE YOU BEEN FRIENDS? 11 years

WHO HAVE YOU BEEN FRIENDS WITH THE LONGEST?

WHERE DID YOU MEET?

HOW MANY YEARS HAVE YOU BEEN FRIENDS?

WHO HAVE YOU BEEN FRIENDS WITH THE LONGEST?

WHERE DID YOU MEET?

HOW MANY YEARS HAVE YOU BEEN FRIENDS?

Make New Friends!

Who is your newest friend?

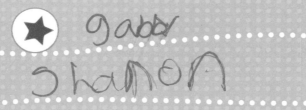

★ gabbr

Shannon

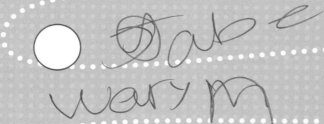

Gabe

wary m

Lan

Lanisha

Teaora

RGB

HAS A FRIEND EVER LET YOU DOWN?

WHAT HAPPENED?
IMPORTANT!
DON'T TELL US WHO —
JUST TELL US HOW!

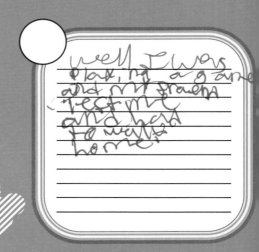

Do you believe
in love
at first sight?

✓ I'm a believer.
○ No way!

○ I'm a believer.
✓ No way!

✓ I'm a believer.
○ No way!

♡ ✓ I'm a believer.
○ No way!

Secret ♥ Crush.

Dare to tell us who?
(We promise not to tell....)

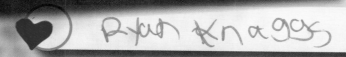 Ryan Knaggs

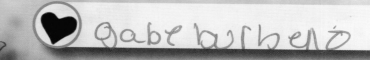 gabe barbero

 Garrett

warren.t

secret guy

30 secret guy
can't tell

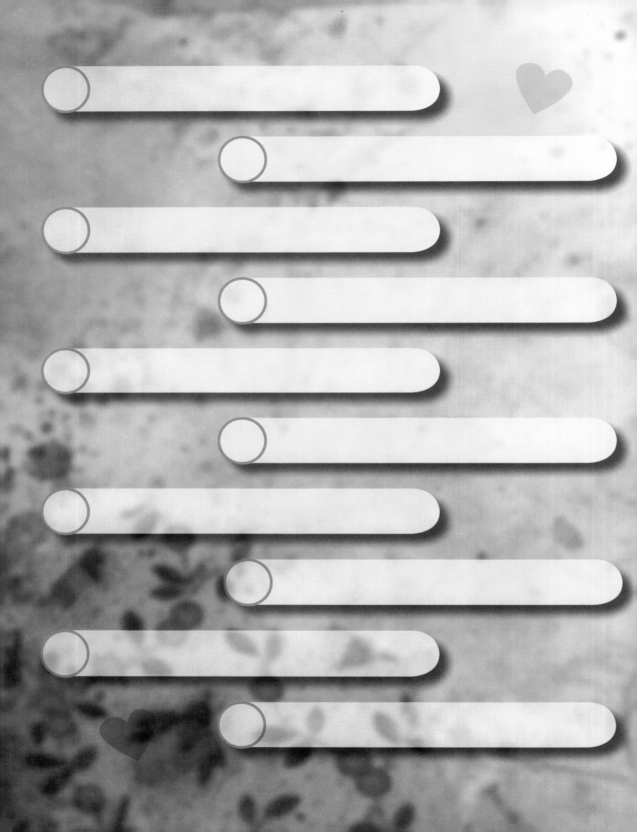

FUTURE PLANS

Where will you be in 5 years?

I will be in
10th grade

What will you be doing?

I will be goin
to school.

How about 20 years?

a real dentis

Where will you be in 5 years?

to prepare
to

What will you be doing?

School

How about 20 years?

real scanne
play

Where will you be in 5 years?

_____

What will you be doing?

_____

How about 20 years?

_____

Where will you be in 5 years?

_____

_____

What will you be doing?

_____

_____

How about 20 years?

_____

Where will you be in 5 years?

_____

_____

What will you be doing?

_____

_____

How about 20 years?

_____

Where will you be in 5 years?

_____

_____

What will you be doing?

_____

_____

How about 20 years?

_____

FUTURE PLANS

FUTURE PLANS

Where will you be in 5 years?

I will be in
10th grade

What will you be doing?

going to school

How about 20 years?

a dentist
not enthuse

Where will you be in 5 years?

10th grade

What will you be doing?

going to school

How about 20 years?

pro scores

Where will you be in 5 years?

What will you be doing?

How about 20 years?

Where will you be in 5 years?

_____

_____

What will you be doing?

_____

_____

How about 20 years?

_____

Where will you be in 5 years?

_____

_____

What will you be doing?

_____

How about 20 years?

_____

Where will you be in 5 years?

_____

_____

What will you be doing?

_____

_____

How about 20 years?

_____

FUTURE PLANS

When I grow up I want to be a dentist.

When I grow up I want to be a nurse.

When I grow up I want to be a mom.

When I grow up I want to be a teacher.

When I grow up I want to be a a gym teacher.

When I grow up I want to be a soccer player.

When I grow up I want to be a _____.

When I grow up I want to be a _____.

When I grow up I want to be a _____.

When I grow up I want to be a _____.

When I grow up I want to be a _____.

When I grow up I want to be a pro soccer player

Where in the world?

If you could travel anywhere in the world, where would you go?

Florida

If you could live anywhere in the world, where would you live?

Jamica or
Calfornia

If you could travel anywhere in the world, where would you go?

Jemakia

If you could live anywhere in the world, where would you live?

Calfornia

If you could travel anywhere in the world, where would you go?

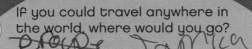
Eropwe Jamica

If you could live anywhere in the world, where would you live?

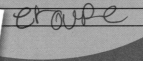
Erope

If you could travel anywhere in the world, where would you go?

If you could live anywhere in the world, where would you live?

If you could travel anywhere in the world, where would you go?
_____
_____

If you could live anywhere in the world, where would you live?
_____
_____

If you could travel anywhere in the world, where would you go?
_____
_____

If you could live anywhere in the world, where would you live?
_____
_____

If you could travel anywhere in the world, where would you go?
_____
_____

If you could live anywhere in the world, where would you live?
_____
_____

If you could travel anywhere in the world, where would you go?
_____
_____

If you could live anywhere in the world, where would you live?
_____
_____

If you could travel anywhere in the world, where would you go?
_____
_____

If you could live anywhere in the world, where would you live?
_____
_____

If you could travel anywhere in the world, where would you go?
_____
_____

If you could live anywhere in the world, where would you live?
_____
_____

Rank these in order of importance.

Health

Wealth

Happiness

1. Happiness
2. Health
3. wealt

1. wealth
2. Happiness
3. Health

1. Health
2. wealth
3. Happiness

1.
2.
3.

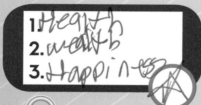

1. Health
2. Wealth
3. Happiness

1.
2.
3.

1.
2.
3.

1.
2.
3.

Shop 'til you drop!

My favorite store is...

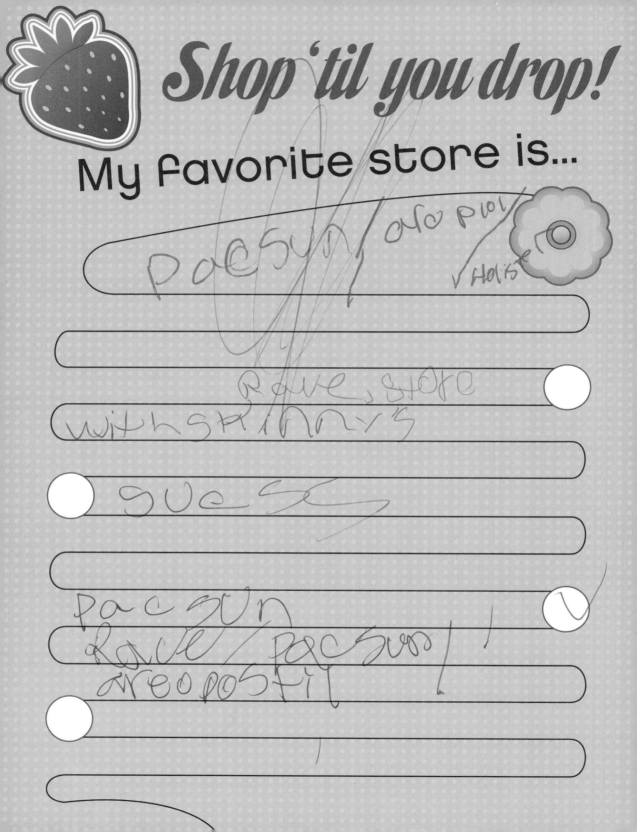

Paesun, aeropo
Holister

Rave, store with skinnys

gues

Pacsun
Rave/Pacsun/
areopostil

paesern, Rave, curco
Postal

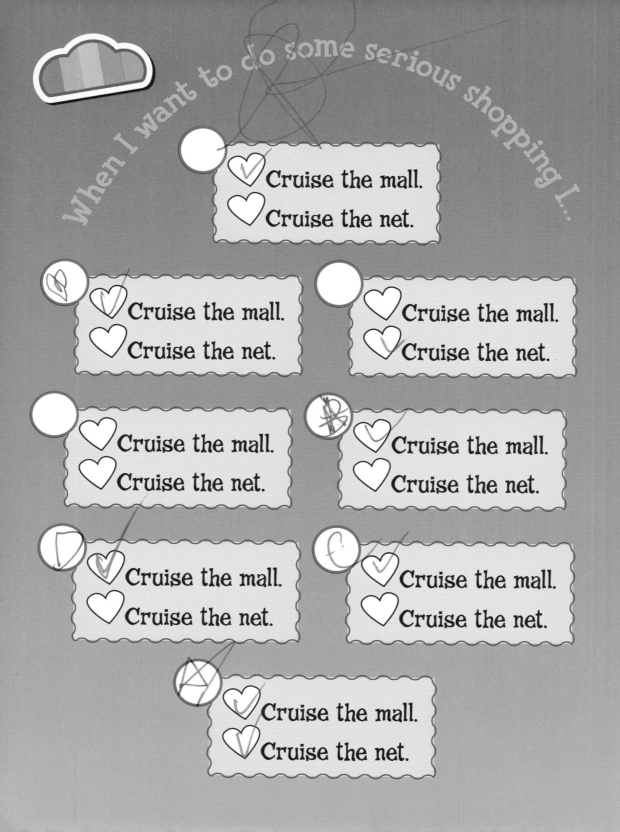

♡ Cruise the mall.
♡ Cruise the net.

♡ Cruise the mall.
♡ Cruise the net.

♡ Cruise the mall.
♡ Cruise the net.

♡ Cruise the mall.
♡ Cruise the net.

♡ Cruise the mall.
♡ Cruise the net.

♡ Cruise the mall.
♡ Cruise the net.

♡ Cruise the mall.
♡ Cruise the net.

♡ Cruise the mall.
♡ Cruise the net.

Quick! How many pairs of shoes do you own?

50

15

√ 2

M 8

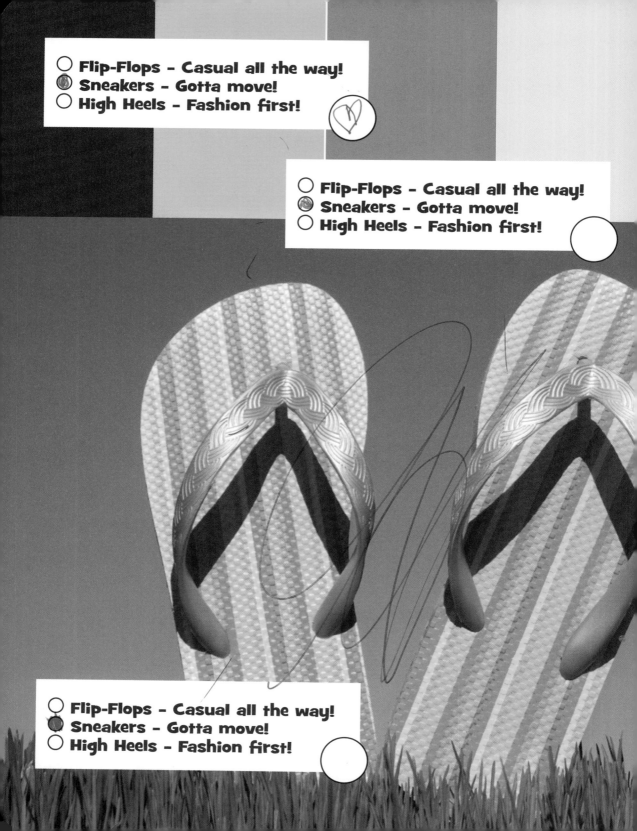

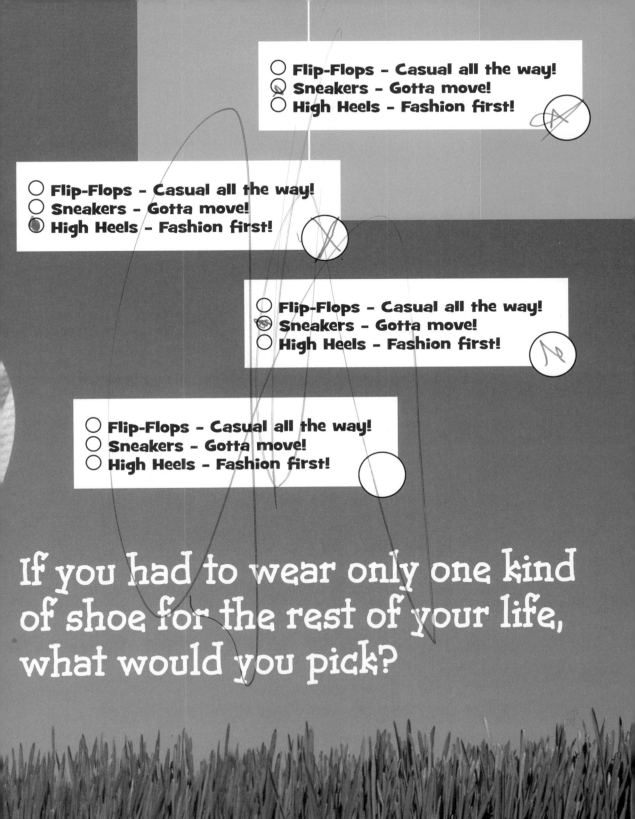

If you had to wear only one kind of shoe for the rest of your life, what would you pick?

- ○ **Flip Flops – Casual all the way!**
- ○ **Sneakers – Gotta move!**
- ○ **High Heels – Fashion first!**

- ○ **Flip Flops – Casual all the way!**
- ○ **Sneakers – Gotta move!**
- ○ **High Heels – Fashion first!**

- ○ **Flip Flops – Casual all the way!**
- ○ **Sneakers – Gotta move!**
- ○ **High Heels – Fashion first!**

○ **Flip Flops – Casual all the way!**
○ **Sneakers – Gotta move!**
○ **High Heels – Fashion first!**

○ **Flip Flops – Casual all the way!**
○ **Sneakers – Gotta move!**
○ **High Heels – Fashion first!**

○ **Flip Flops – Casual all the way!**
○ **Sneakers – Gotta move!**
○ **High Heels – Fashion first!**

○ **Flip Flops – Casual all the way!**
○ **Sneakers – Gotta move!**
○ **High Heels – Fashion first!**

Sketch your dream outfit here...

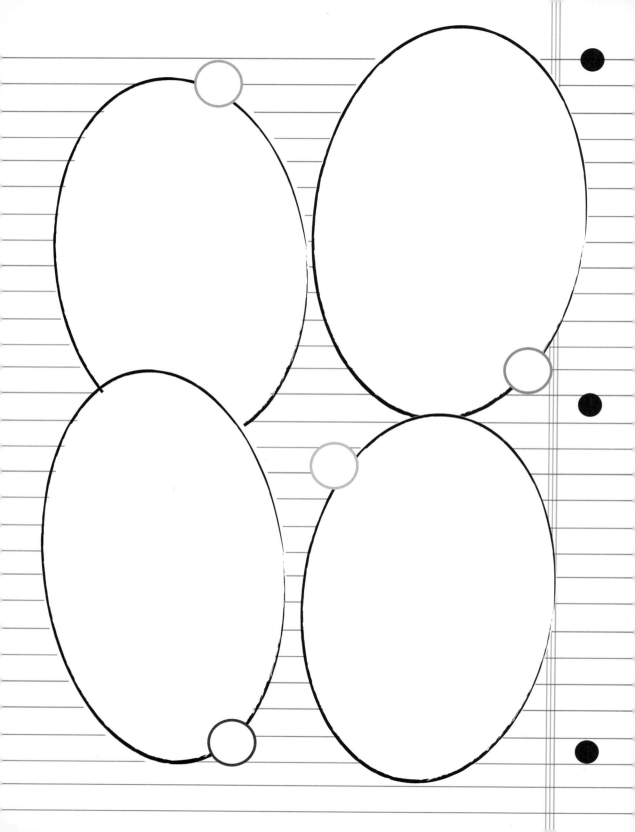

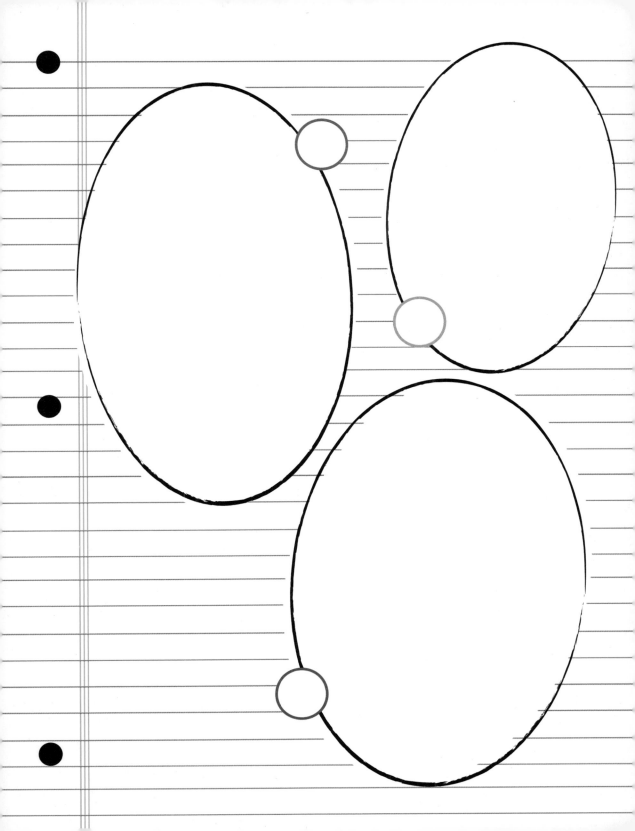

AMERICA'S NEXT
top model
or
project
RUNWAY
(What's your favorite?)

Pros ect Runway

project Runway

project Runway

A

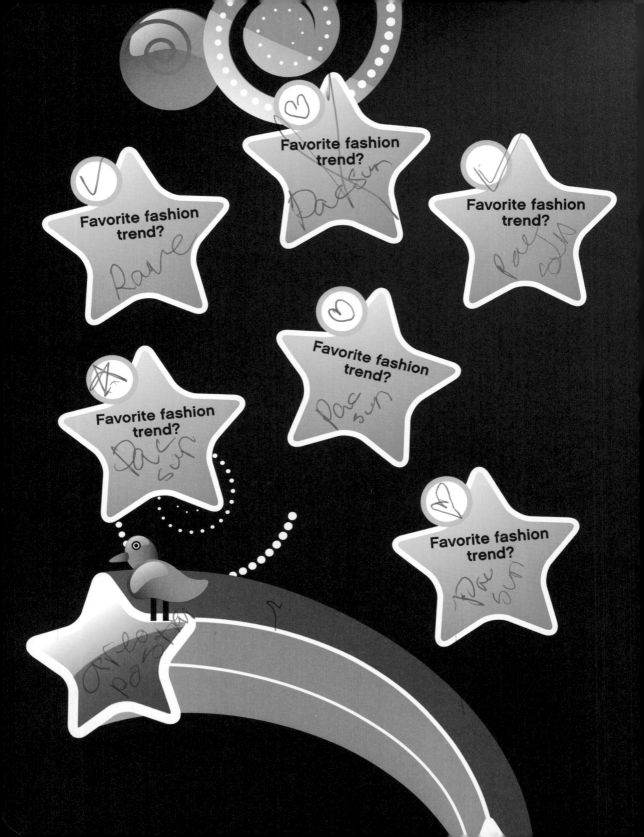

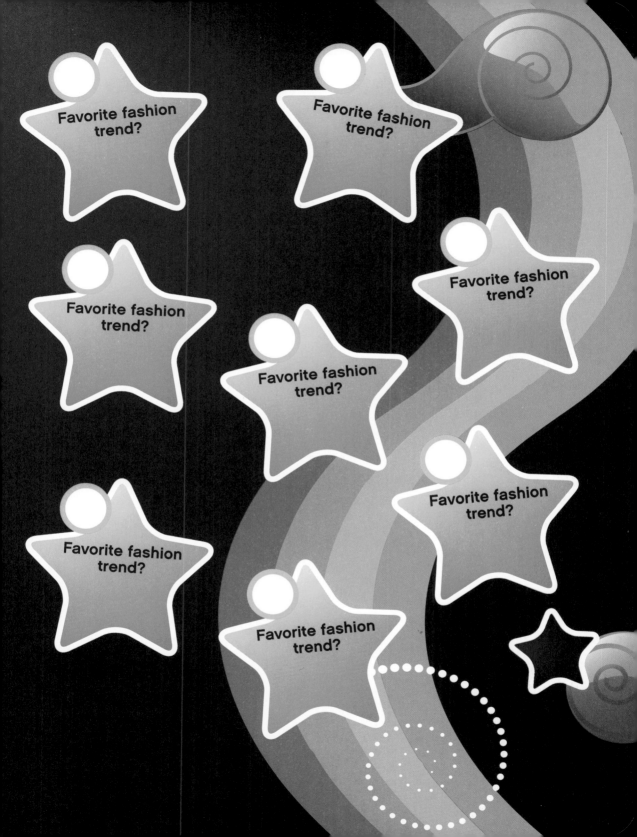

SWEATSHIRT or Sweater?

Sweat Shirt ◯

Sweater ◯

Sweat Shirt ◯

S,weater ◯

◯

◯

◯

◯

◯

◯

skinny JEANS or Skirt?

Skirt ⭕

Skirt ⭕

Skinny Jeans ♡

⭕

⭕

⭕

⭕

⭕

⭕

⭕

Hair and there.

Usually I wear my hair...

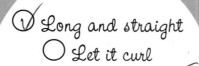 Long and straight
○ Let it curl
○ Just a simple ponytail
○ Other
halfuporhalfdown

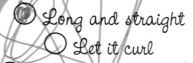 Long and straight
○ Let it curl
○ Just a simple ponytail
○ Other
_____

☑ Long and straight
◯ Let it curl
◯ Just a simple ponytail
◯ Other Short and ___ wth bang

☑ Long and straight
◯ Let it curl
◯ Just a simple ponytail
◯ Other _____

☑ Long and straight
☑ Let it curl
◯ Just a simple ponytail
◯ Other _____

○ Long and straight
○ Let it curl
○ Just a simple ponytail
○ Other _____

○ Long and straight
○ Let it curl
○ Just a simple ponytail
○ Other
_____

○ Long and straight
○ Let it curl
○ Just a simple ponytail
○ Other
_____

- ◯ Long and straight
- ◯ Let it curl
- ◯ Just a simple ponytail
- ◯ Other _____

- ◯ Long and straight
- ◯ Let it curl
- ◯ Just a simple ponytail
- ◯ Other _____

- ◯ Long and straight
- ◯ Let it curl
- ◯ Just a simple ponytail
- ◯ Other _____

Favorite Flicks

Scariest Movie _Holween 8_
Funniest Movie _Diary of a wimpy Kid Dog series_
Most Romantic Movie _Brate/Roll bounce_
Best Movie Ever! _Diaros a wimpy Kid_

Scariest Movie _Holloween_
Funniest Movie _Diary of a wimpy Kid_
Most Romantic Movie _Roll Downer_
Best Movie Ever! _Bratz_

Scariest Movie _____
Funniest Movie _____
Most Romantic Movie _____
Best Movie Ever! _____

PRODUCTION

ROLL   SCENE   TAKE

DIRECTOR

Scariest Movie_____
Funniest Movie_____
Most Romantic Movie _____
Best Movie Ever! _____

Scariest Movie_____
Funniest Movie_____
Most Romantic Movie _____
Best Movie Ever! _____

Scariest Movie_____
Funniest Movie_____
Most Romantic Movie _____
Best Movie Ever! _____

Scariest Movie_____
Funniest Movie_____
Most Romantic Movie _____
Best Movie Ever! _____

Scariest Movie_____
Funniest Movie_____
Most Romantic Movie _____
Best Movie Ever! _____

Scariest Movie _____
Funniest Movie _____
Most Romantic Movie _____
Best Movie Ever! _____

Scariest Movie _____
Funniest Movie _____
Most Romantic Movie _____
Best Movie Ever! _____

Scariest Movie _____
Funniest Movie _____
Most Romantic Movie _____
Best Movie Ever! _____

Scariest Movie _____
Funniest Movie _____
Most Romantic Movie _____
Best Movie Ever! _____

PRODUCTION

ROLL | SCENE | TAKE

DIRECTOR

DATE

Scariest Movie_____
Funniest Movie_____
Most Romantic Movie _____
Best Movie Ever! _____

Scariest Movie_____
Funniest Movie_____
Most Romantic Movie _____
Best Movie Ever! _____

Scariest Movie_____
Funniest Movie_____
Most Romantic Movie _____
Best Movie Ever! _____

Scariest Movie_____
Funniest Movie_____
Most Romantic Movie _____
Best Movie Ever! _____

Scariest Movie_____
Funniest Movie_____
Most Romantic Movie _____
Best Movie Ever! _____

Best movie based on
a book
Diary of a wimpy kid

Did you like the book
or movie better?
The movie

Best movie based on
a book
Diary of a wimpy kid

Did you like the book
or movie better?
The book

Best movie based on
a book
_____

Did you like the book
or movie better?
_____

Best movie based on
a book
_____

Did you like the book
or movie better?
_____

Best movie based on
a book
_____

Did you like the book
or movie better?
_____

Best movie based on
a book
_____

Did you like the book
or movie better?
_____

Best movie based on
a book
_____

Did you like the book
or movie better?
_____

Best movie based on
a book
_____

Did you like the book
or movie better?
_____

Best movie based on
a book
_____

Did you like the book
or movie better?
_____

Best movie based on
a book
_____

Did you like the book
or movie better?
_____

Your Name in Lights!

If they made a movie of your life, who would play you?

Larisha

April

Shenon

Teara

Jemare

Sing a Song

BEST SONG OF THE YEAR

1 less 1 on babby

BEST SONG OF ALL TIME

1 less 1 onlygirl

BEST SONG OF THE YEAR

baby

BEST SONG OF ALL TIME

1 less onlygirl

BEST SONG OF THE YEAR

BEST SONG OF ALL TIME

BEST SONG OF THE YEAR

BEST SONG OF ALL TIME

BEST SONG OF THE YEAR

_____

BEST SONG OF ALL TIME

BEST SONG OF THE YEAR

_____

BEST SONG OF ALL TIME

BEST SONG OF THE YEAR

_____

BEST SONG OF ALL TIME

BEST SONG OF THE YEAR

_____

BEST SONG OF ALL TIME

BEST SONG OF THE YEAR

_____

BEST SONG OF ALL TIME

BEST SONG OF THE YEAR

_____

BEST SONG OF ALL TIME

Book Nook

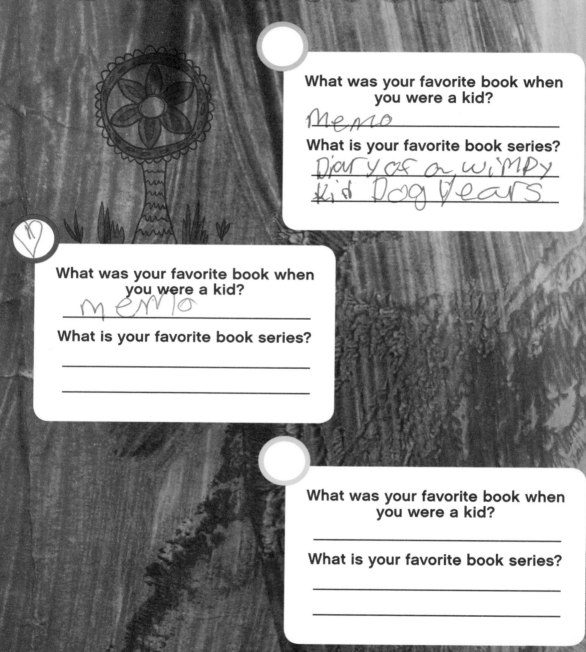

What was your favorite book when you were a kid?

MEMO

What is your favorite book series?

Diary of a wimpy
Kid Dog Years

What was your favorite book when you were a kid?

MEMO

What is your favorite book series?

What was your favorite book when you were a kid?

What is your favorite book series?

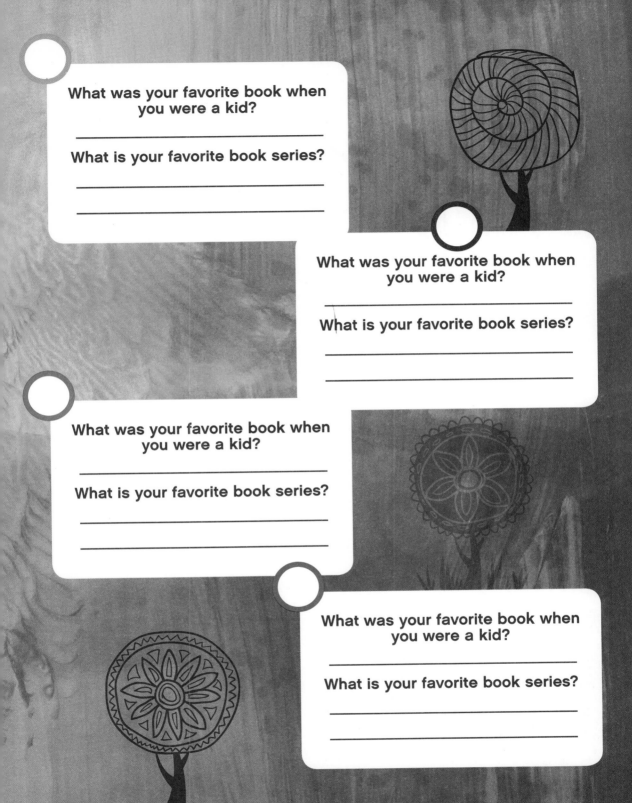

What was your favorite book when you were a kid?

_____

What is your favorite book series?

_____

_____

What was your favorite book when you were a kid?

_____

What is your favorite book series?

_____

_____

What was your favorite book when you were a kid?

_____

What is your favorite book series?

_____

_____

What was your favorite book when you were a kid?

_____

What is your favorite book series?

_____

_____

BOOK DESIGNER

Design a new cover for your favorite book.

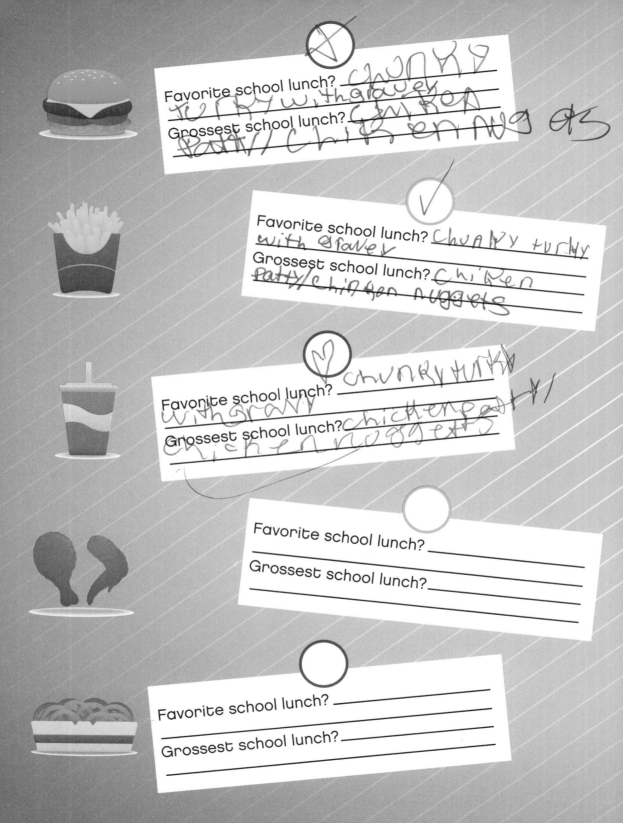

Favorite school lunch? _CHUNKY_
TURKY with gravey
Grossest school lunch? _CHICKEN_
Patty/ChiKen nuggets

Favorite school lunch? _CHUNKY turMy_
with gravey
Grossest school lunch? _Chicken_
Patty/chicken nuggets

Favorite school lunch? _CHUNKY TURKY_
with gravy
Grossest school lunch? _chicken patty/_
chicken nuggets

Favorite school lunch? _____
_____
Grossest school lunch? _____
_____

Favorite school lunch? _____
_____
Grossest school lunch? _____
_____

Favorite school lunch? _____
_____
Grossest school lunch? _____
_____

Favorite school lunch? _____
_____
Grossest school lunch? _____
_____

Favorite school lunch? _____
_____
Grossest school lunch? _____
_____

Favorite school lunch? _____
Grossest school lunch? _____
_____

Favorite school lunch? _____
Grossest school lunch? _____
_____

Food Fight...

☐ NO WAY! ☑ CAN'T WAIT!

☐ NO WAY! ☑ CAN'T WAIT!

☐ NO WAY! ☑ CAN'T WAIT!

☐ NO WAY! ☑ CAN'T WAIT!

☐ NO WAY! ☑ CAN'T WAIT!

☐ NO WAY! ☑ CAN'T WAIT!

☐ NO WAY! ☑ CAN'T WAIT!

☐ NO WAY! ☑ CAN'T WAIT!

☐ NO WAY! ☑ CAN'T WAIT!

☐ NO WAY! ☑ CAN'T WAIT!

☑ **NO Way!** ☐ **CAN'T Wait!**

☐ **NO Way!** ☑ **CAN'T Wait!**

☑ **NO Way!** ☐ **CAN'T Wait!**

☑ **NO Way!** ☐ **CAN'T Wait!**

☑ **NO Way!** ☑ **CAN'T Wait!**

☑ **NO Way!** ☑ **CAN'T Wait!**

☑ **NO Way!** ☐ **CAN'T Wait!**

☐ **NO Way!** ☑ **CAN'T Wait!**

☑ **NO Way!** ☐ **CAN'T Wait!**

☑ **NO Way!** ☐ **CAN'T Wait!**

Chocolate or Vanilla? _vanilla_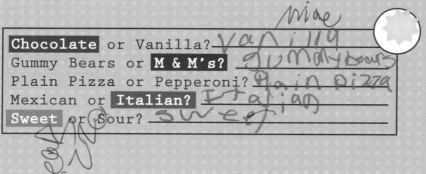
Gummy Bears or **M & M's?** _Gummy Bears_
Plain Pizza or Pepperoni? _Plain pizza_
Mexican or **Italian?** _Italian_
Sweet or Sour? _sweet_

Chocolate or Vanilla? _vanilla_
Gummy Bears or **M & M's?** _M&M"s_
Plain Pizza or Pepperoni? _Pepperoni_
Mexican or **Italian?** _Italian_
Sweet or Sour? _sweet_

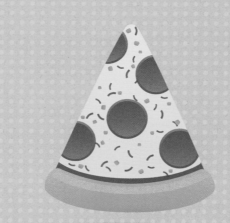

Chocolate or Vanilla?
Gummy Bears or **M & M's?**
Plain Pizza or Pepperoni?
Mexican or **Italian?**
Sweet or Sour?

Chocolate or Vanilla?
Gummy Bears or **M & M's?**
Plain Pizza or Pepperoni?
Mexican or **Italian?**
Sweet or Sour?

Chocolate or Vanilla? _Chocolate_
Gummy Bears or **M & M's?** _M&M's_
Plain Pizza or Pepperoni? _Plain/chicken_
Mexican or **Italian?** _Italian_
Sweet or Sour? _sweet_

Chocolate or Vanilla? Vanilla
Gummy Bears or **M & M's?** Gummy bears
Plain Pizza or Pepperoni? Pepperoni
Mexican or **Italian?** Italian
Sweet or Sour? Sweet

Chocolate or Vanilla? Vanilla
Gummy Bears or **M & M's?** Gummy bears
Plain Pizza or Pepperoni? Plain pizza
Mexican or **Italian?** Italian
Sweet or Sour? Sweet

Chocolate or Vanilla?
Gummy Bears or **M & M's?**
Plain Pizza or Pepperoni?
Mexican or **Italian?**
Sweet or Sour?

Chocolate or Vanilla?
Gummy Bears or **M & M's?**
Plain Pizza or Pepperoni?
Mexican or **Italian?**
Sweet or Sour?

Chocolate or Vanilla?
Gummy Bears or **M & M's?**
Plain Pizza or Pepperoni?
Mexican or **Italian?**
Sweet or Sour?

Chocolate or Vanilla?————————
Gummy Bears or **M & M's?** ——————
Plain Pizza or Pepperoni? ——————
Mexican or **Italian?** ——————
Sweet or Sour? ——————

Chocolate or Vanilla?————————
Gummy Bears or **M & M's?** ——————
Plain Pizza or Pepperoni? ——————
Mexican or **Italian?** ——————
Sweet or Sour? ——————

Chocolate or Vanilla?
Gummy Bears or **M & M's?**
Plain Pizza or Pepperoni?
Mexican or **Italian?**
Sweet or Sour?

Chocolate or Vanilla?
Gummy Bears or **M & M's?**
Plain Pizza or Pepperoni?
Mexican or **Italian?**
Sweet or Sour?

Chocolate or Vanilla?————————
Gummy Bears or **M & M's?** ——————
Plain Pizza or Pepperoni? ——————
Mexican or **Italian?** ——————
Sweet or Sour? ——————

Chocolate or Vanilla?

Gummy Bears or **M & M's?**

Plain Pizza or Pepperoni?

Mexican or **Italian?**

Sweet or Sour?

Chocolate or Vanilla?

Gummy Bears or **M & M's?**

Plain Pizza or Pepperoni?

Mexican or **Italian?**

Sweet or Sour?

Chocolate or Vanilla?

Gummy Bears or **M & M's?**

Plain Pizza or Pepperoni?

Mexican or **Italian?**

Sweet or Sour?

Chocolate or Vanilla?

Gummy Bears or **M & M's?**

Plain Pizza or Pepperoni?

Mexican or **Italian?**

Sweet or Sour?

Chocolate or Vanilla?

Gummy Bears or **M & M's?**

Plain Pizza or Pepperoni?

Mexican or **Italian?**

Sweet or Sour?

And the award goes to...

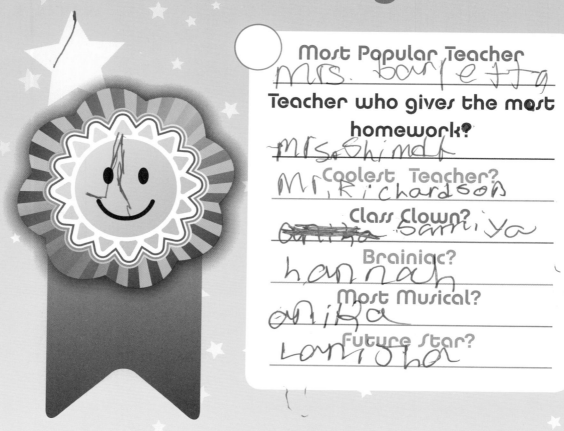

Most Popular Teacher
Mrs. Barletta

Teacher who gives the most homework?
Mrs. Shindt

Coolest Teacher?
Mr. Richardson

Class Clown?
Samiya

Brainiac?
hannah

Most Musical?
anika

Future Star?
Lanisha

Most Popular Teacher Mr. Richardson

Teacher who gives the most homework? Mrs. Sparks

Coolest Teacher? Mrs. Richardson

Class Clown? anna Darian

Brainiac? aniia Tilman

Most Musical? Lanisha

Future Star? Lanisha

Most Popular Teacher _____

Teacher who gives the most homework? _____

Coolest Teacher? _____

Class Clown? _____

Brainiac? _____

Most Musical? _____

Future Star? _____

Most Popular Teacher
_____

Teacher who gives the most homework?
_____

Coolest Teacher?
_____

Class Clown?
_____

Brainiac?
_____

Most Musical?
_____

Future Star?
_____

Most Popular Teacher

Teacher who gives the most homework?

Coolest Teacher?

Class Clown?

Brainiac?

Most Musical?

Future Star?

Most Popular Teacher _____

Teacher who gives the most homework? _____

Coolest Teacher? _____

Class Clown? _____

Brainiac? _____

Most Musical? _____

Future Star? _____

Most Popular Teacher _____

Teacher who gives the most homework? _____

Coolest Teacher? _____

Class Clown? _____

Brainiac? _____

Most Musical? _____

Future Star? _____

Most Popular Teacher

_____

Teacher who gives the most homework?

_____

Coolest Teacher?

_____

Class Clown?

_____

Brainiac?

_____

Most Musical?

_____

Future Star?

_____

Most Popular Teacher

Teacher who gives the most homework?

Coolest Teacher?

Class Clown?

Brainiac?

Most Musical?

Future Star?

Most Popular Teacher _____

Teacher who gives the most homework? _____

Coolest Teacher? _____

Class Clown? _____

Brainiac? _____

Most Musical? _____

Future Star? _____

Most Popular Teacher _____

Teacher who gives the most homework? _____

Coolest Teacher? _____

Class Clown? _____

Brainiac? _____

Most Musical? _____

Future Star? _____

Most Popular Teacher
_____

Teacher who gives the most homework?
_____

Coolest Teacher?
_____

Class Clown?
_____

Brainiac?
_____

Most Musical?
_____

Future Star?
_____

Most Popular Teacher
Mr. Richardson

Teacher who gives the most homework?
Mrs. Barletta

Coolest Teacher?
Mr. Richardson

Class Clown?
Sam/Selby

Brainiac?
Hannah

Most Musical?
Anika

Future Star?
Lanisha/one

Most Popular Teacher Mr. Rone

Teacher who gives the most homework? Mrs. Barletta

Coolest Teacher? Mr. Richardson

Class Clown? Travon

Brainiac? ~~Jaz~~ i. Zi

Most Musical? Anika

Future Star? Lanisha

Most Popular Teacher _____

Teacher who gives the most homework? _____

Coolest Teacher? _____

Class Clown? _____

Brainiac? _____

Most Musical? _____

Future Star? _____

Most Popular Teacher

_____

Teacher who gives the most homework?

_____

Coolest Teacher?

_____

Class Clown?

_____

Brainiac?

_____

Most Musical?

_____

Future Star?

_____

Last chance...
Leave your
autograph here!

For this page
1 out of order this
line is out of order.

April Atkins B.K.A. Triple A